"I have a van," said Dan.

“I am not a vet,” said Dan.
“But I can help pets.”

“I have a big dog,” said Val.
“Can you help him?”

"Yes, I can!" said Dan.

Val's dog Fuzz gets into the van.

“I have to rub, rub, rub you!”
said Dan.

“You did it!” said Val.

"I have the best pet and you have the best van!"